MW00488485

IN SEARCH OF MEDIOCRITY

IN SEARCH OF MEDIOCRITY

Forty-nine ways to reduce your company to insignificance

by Philip B. Nelson, K. Michael Schmidt
Milton A. Stubbs
illustrations by Signe Wilkinson

WOODSIDE PRESS, Mountain View, CA

WOODSIDE PRESS
MOUNTAIN VIEW, CALIFORNIA

Inquiries should be addressed to Woodside Press,
105 South Drive, Suite D, Mountain View, CA 94040.
Printed in the United States of America.

Library of Congress Cataloging in Publication Data

Nelson, Philip B.
In search of mediocrity.

1. Business—Anecdotes, facetiae, satire, etc.
2. Business—Caricatures and cartoons. 3. Management—Anecdotes, facetiae, satire, etc. 4. Management Caricatures and cartoons. I. Schmidt, K. Michael, 1934-
II. Stubbs, Milton A., 1936- III. Wilkinson, Signe, 1950- IV. Title.
PN6231.B85N45 1986 741.5′973 85-26417

ISBN 0-9615870-0-8

First Edition

This book is dedicated to those who have a bone-deep belief in negativity.

These silent friends, who work daily inside our corporations to turn the positive into the negative, are the true believers who understand that a corporation should never grow beyond the Mom and Pop Shop. These unsung heroes are uninnovative and elusive; they avoid and demean the customer and try diligently to avoid individual commitment; but they do have a unique value system. It is this pervasive system in American business which fosters criticizing, complaining and condemning and pays big dividends in reducing complex organizations and Fortune 500 companies to their original, more stable and healthy states—the garages from whence they sprung.

With this book, the authors thank these unsung heroes.

Create an atmosphere
of trust.

Attract customers
with prompt service.

BE BACK IN
5 MINUTES

Share your corporate role models with your employees.

KHADAFY
IDI
WELCOME!

Get your employees
to know you intimately.

Keep in mind the importance of your technical staff.

WOULD YOU KINDLY REQUEST, IF IT'S NOT ANY TROUBLE, WHETHER MR. TAYLOR MIGHT SPARE ME A MINUTE. I'M MR. TRUEHART, er JACK, UH, THE COMPANY PRESIDENT, if you please....
M.I.S.

Listen to your people.

Foster a strong customer base!

WHAT'S YOUR GRIPE, LADY?

COMPLAINTS

NO RETURNS WITHOUT AFFIDAVIT FROM THE ATTORNEY GENERAL

THE MERCHANT IS USUALLY RIGHT

EXCHANGES? DON'T EVEN THINK ABOUT IT.

Show employees that
everyone is valued equally.

PRES.
VISITORS
FAVORED LIEUTENANTS
LOYAL DEPUTIES
DRONES

Foster entrepreneurship.

BRILLIANT! TOO BAD IT'S NOT IN YOUR MBO.
THEM
US

Stay close to the customer.

WAIT 'TIL YOU SEE OUR NEW DISC DRIVES, DAVE. I MEAN– YOU'LL LOVE 'EM...
SALES

Recognize the importance
of cordial telephone manners.

RATHER, MATHER, AND LIPPINCOTT..... JUST A SEC, I'LL CHECK.
I'M SOOOO SORRY. MR. MATHER IS OFF THIS AFTERNOON.

Create an atmosphere
of warmth and belonging.

SHOW I.D.
DID YOU PARK IN THE RIGHT SPACE?
EMPLOYEES MUST SHOW IDs
GUARD DOG ON DUTY
WELCOME

Maintain an adequate
staff of analysts.

MANUFACTURING
RECEIVING ANALYST
INVENTORY ANALYST
PRICING ANALYST
INPUTTING ANALYST
PARTS ANALYST
DISTRIBUTION ANALYST
JUST-TO-MAKE-SURE ANALYST
RELEASING ANALYST
Pat
Pat
Pat
WIDGETS

Surround yourself
with talented relatives.

HAWLEY
MANUFACTURING
INC.

HAWLEY
HAW
HAW
Hawley
VICE PRES.
HAWLEY
TREASURER
HAWLEY
PRESIDENT
HAWLEY

Offer an “open door” management policy.

NOT RESPONSIBLE FOR LOST OR DAMAGED EGOS.
ENTER AT YOUR OWN RISK

Cater to your employees'
nutritional needs.

JACK'S
MY-T-FINE
CAFETERIA

Convey the
corporate culture.

ONCE UPON A TIME
IN A GARAGE
NEAR
PALO ALTO...
THE COMPANY STORY

Encourage communication.

If it ain’t broke,
don’t fix it.

Coca-Cola®

Develop a corporate stress management program.

DEPOSIT COINS
VALIUM
LIBRIUM
DARVON

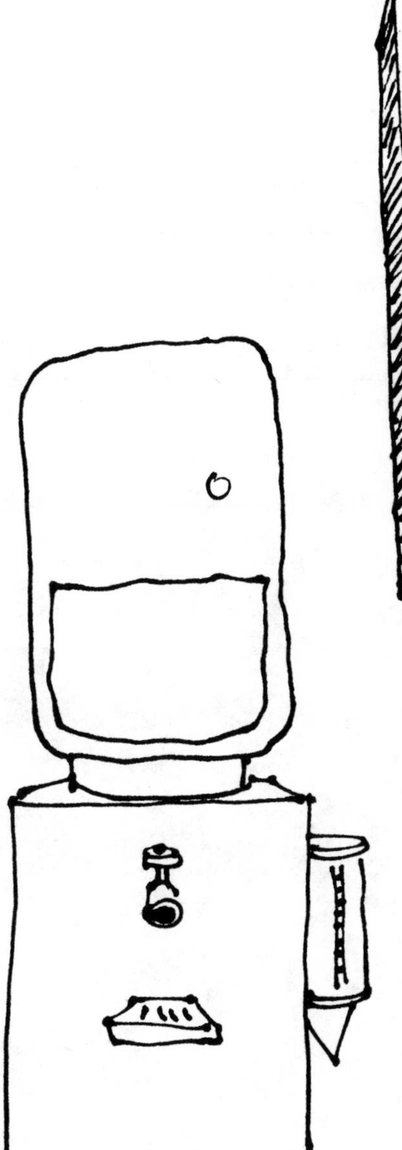

Institute a bias
for action.

BUY! SELL! BUY! BUY! SELL!
DAVIS! YOU'RE FIRED! SMITH! YOU'RE TRANSFERRED! LANDAU....
SHIP TO:

Create an atmosphere
of equality.

July
THERE'S NO WOMAN LIKE A NAKED WOMAN

Practice "management by walking around."

You seem to be having a hard time concentrating, Peyton...

Attend to
the simple amenities.

LADIES ROOM
NO LOITERING

Simplify communication.

I TRACKED DOWN THE PROBLEM WITH YOUR FULL DUPLEX SYNCHRONUS MODUM. SEEMS YOUR ASCCI FILE HAD A PARITY ERROR IN THE FIRST BYTE OF THE DIRECTORY SECTOR.

COME AGAIN?

Foster a sense
of job security.

HIGGINS
SMITH
LANDAU
LANDAU

Incorporate physical fitness
in your company's workday.

MR. JENKINS
WILL BE WITH YOU
IN 20 REPS.

Focus on the positive.

SALES ARE UP 200%,
PRODUCTION COSTS ARE DOWN,
AND I GOT THE PRODUCT
ON THE COVER OF
BUSINESS WEEK.

YOUR
SHOELACE
IS UNTIED.

Make jobs more challenging
by introducing
the latest technology.

1966
OK, MISS PETREL.
TAKE A LETTER.
1986
OK, MS. PETREL.
TAKE A LETTER.

Encourage bold, new thinking.

Keep it simple, stupid.

IN CASE OF FIRE:

1. CALL PLANT MANAGER (CHECK STAFF DIRECTORY)
2. FILL OUT MEMO
3. FILE COPIES WITH MAINTENANCE
4. REPORT TO SUPERVISOR
5. BREAK GLASS
6. SOUND ALARM

Let your employees know where they stand.

TRAP DOOR

Stand behind your product.

TIME TO TAKE THIS BABY BACK FOR A CIRCUIT FIX... OUR EXPENSE, OF COURSE!
ACE MEDI-SYSTEMS

Foster a positive
sales approach.

BOB'S CARS
Like New
HI! I'M BOB!
CONTRACT

Update your
technology regularly.

LOOKS LIKE THEY'VE
MASTERED THAT PROGRAM.
TIME FOR A
SYSTEMS UPGRADE!

Hire the best
the business schools
have to offer.

BY THE WAY, MR. WEATHERSOME, WHAT IS OUR PRODUCT?
STANF
HARVARD

Incorporate the latest in Japanese management theory.

LEAVE YOUR SHOES BY THE DOOR, RITTER-SAN.
PRESIDENT

Encourage creative idea sharing.

RESEARCH DEPARTMENT

Develop an atmosphere of participation.

the boss
I BELIEVE YOU'RE NEXT, MR. CASEY.
receptionist

Incorporate the latest
in business systems.

FIVE LINKS OF MILD SAUSAGE, PLEASE.

RIGHTO! I'll JUST LOG ON TO MY MANAGEMENT CONTROL PROGRAM...

CALL UP INVENTORY...

AND IT READS OUT OUR CURRENT

STOCK.

SORRY. WE'VE ONLY GOT 3 LINKS LEFT.
MILD

Organize your time along the "one minute manager" model.

FEEL FREE
TO UNBURDEN YOURSELF,
JACOBS.
YOU HAVE
SIXTY
SECONDS!

Maintain an active training program.

MR. HIMMEL IS AT PHONE CLASS.
MR. WARNER AND MS. ELDER ARE LEARNING THE NEW RESEARCH PROGRAM.
MR. TROUNSTINE IS IN COMPUTER TRAINING.
MAY I HELP YOU?
ROSE

Keep a simple form
and lean staff.

ADMINISTRA
MANU-
FACTURING
ACCTNG
PERSONNEL
FINANCE
ADVERTI
SALES

Keep customers
with courteous service.

I CAN'T HELP YOU, SIR, IF YOU REFUSE TO TELL ME WHAT YOU WANT.
BE BACK IN 5 MINUTES

Try creative incentives.

TOP SALESPERSON GETS A NEW CALCULATOR!!
TOP SALESPERSON GETS A DINNER WITH THE BOSS!!
ZZZZZ
TOP SALESPERSON GETS A $5000 RAISE.

Maintain accessibility
at the top.

THE
EXALTED
ONE
IS IN

Speed communication
with the latest
in telephone technology.

YOU HAVE THE WRONG EXTENSION. JUST A SEC AND I'll TRANSFER YOU TO MR. YOST.
**3
NAAA NAAA NAAA NAAA NAAAA NAAA NAAA NAAA NAAA...
3
NAAA NAAA NAAA NAAA NAAA NAAA NAAA NAAA
3*3
NAAA NAAA NAAA NAA NAAA NAAA NAAA...
YO, PHIL!! THERE'S A CALL FOR YOU ON LINE 4.

Remember, product quality
speaks for itself.

CARS
Service

Let employees know
their opinions count.

Suggestion
Box

About the Authors:

Philip B. Nelson, Ph.D., is currently senior vice president of Interdatum, Inc. and is a well known corporate psychologist. He has published a variety of articles and textual materials and is recognized for his workshops on managerial selection and achieving superior managerial performance.

K. Michael Schmidt, Ph.D., is a clinical psychologist specializing in working with key corporate executives. His clients range from individuals to Fortune 500 companies. In addition to his consulting practice, he is and has been an author, corporate president and college professor. Dr. Schmidt has lived in the San Francisco Bay Area for the past 20 years.

Milton A. "Cap" Stubbs is a marketing executive with a Fortune 500 company. He holds a masters degree and is educated in both technical and business areas. His business career spans 25 years in high technology and he lectures on innovation and the sales and marketing of high technology products.

Signe Wilkinson is currently a cartoonist with the *Philadelphia Daily News*. She has been a media cartoonist for a number of years on both the East and West Coasts and has contributed cartoon illustrations for numerous newspapers, books and magazines.